LAUGH IT OFF

Laugh it Off

CARTOONS FROM THE
SATURDAY EVENING POST

EDITED BY

MARIONE R. DERRICKSON

WHITTLESEY HOUSE
MCGRAW-HILL BOOK COMPANY, INC.
London   New York

LAUGH IT OFF

Copyright, 1944, *by the* McGraw-Hill Book Company, Inc.

*This book is produced in full compliance
with the government's regulations for con-
serving paper and other essential materials.*

PUBLISHED BY WHITTLESEY HOUSE

A division of the McGraw-Hill Book Company, Inc.

Printed in the United States of America by Sackett and Wilhelms, Inc.

TO MY DAUGHTER

ALICE JANE

May She Keep Her Sense of Humor

She'll Need It

ACKNOWLEDGMENTS

I should like to express my appreciation to all the cartoonists who were good enough to let me include their material in this book.

FOREWORD

Those of us who are not cartoonists open our newspapers at breakfast, approve, view with alarm, chuckle, groan or pound the table, depending on whether the news tickles our particular prejudices or treads on our toes.

The cartoonist, however, approaches the day's events with a professionally jaundiced eye, a pencil eager to stalk its quarry and the sober conviction that there's a gag somewhere in that newspaper if he can find it and put it over.

He finds it all right, because more than 100,000 sketches come to Independence Square annually, and often enough he puts it over because the POST alone publishes nearly 1300 cartoons in the course of a year.

This is a collection taken from more than 100 issues of the POST and I have tried to present as wide a selection as possible with the realization that humor more than any other commodity must satisfy a variety of tastes.

I hope you'll enjoy *Laugh It Off*.

MARIONE R. DERRICKSON
Post Scripts Editor

Philadelphia

LIST OF ARTISTS

Alain, Daniel,
Allen, Colin,

Angelo, Emidio,
Atkins, Elmer,

Bailey, John,
Barlow, Tony,
Beaven, Frank,
Boltinoff, Henry,
Borgstedt, Douglas,
Brown, Bo,
Brown, Scott,

Carr, Gene,
Cartwright, Chas.,

Coe, Roland,
Corka,

Day, Chon,
Day, Robert,
Darrow, Whitney,
Dell, R. C.,
deSarro, Rodney,
Dove, Leonard,

Ericson, Eric,

Fallon, Norman,
Fuller, Ving, 52

Gallivan, Bob,
Garel, Leo,
Garrity, Martin,
Garza, Ernie,
Gerard, Dave,
Gibson, Mary,
Green, G. H.,
Graham, Ed,

Haenigsen, H. W.,
Herman, Vic,
Huffine, Dave,
Hunter, Ed,

Jamme, Louis,
Johnson, Will,

Kalbach, John,
Kaunus, A. John,
Keate, Jeff,
Keller, Reamer,
Ketcham, Hank,
Key, Ted,

King, Bill,

Lariar, Larry,
Linn, Bandel,
Lundberg, Gustav,
Lusinger, Chas.,

Machamer, Jeff,
Marge,
McKay, Dorothy,
Merrylen,
Middlecamp, Herb,
Mossler, Arnie,

Nofziger, Ed,

O'Malley, Bill,
Owen, Frank,

Partch, Vip,
Peters, Eric,
Platt, Charles,
Price, George,
Price, John M.,

Rea, Gardner,
Reckas, George,
Reynolds, Larry,
Richter, Mischa,

Roir, Irving,
Rose, Carl,
Rosol, John,
Ross, Al,
Roth, Ben,
Ruble, Bill,

Salo,
Schus, Adolph,
Shellhase, Geo.,
Shermund, Barbara,
Smith, George,
Soderlund, Mel,
Stanley, Gene,
Stiles, Kirk,

Terry, Hilda,
Trent, W. P.,

Walter, Linda,
White, Hugh E., Jr.,
Wilkinson, Fritz,
Wolfe, George,

Young, Alex,

"He just took his first step. It was a pip."

"No more for me, thanks. I've got to drive home."

"Madame is fed up with this country, and wishes to know *where* she can go to. Will you have the pleasure of telling her, Mr. Finnis, or shall I?"

"A Gremlin is a little elfin creature that hinders the progress of a pilot. For instance—"

Drawn by Colin Allen

"Don't say anything. I think they're just trying to attract
our attention."

"So I told him he came from an egg. How I dread the next question!"

"Mom, can I have just one more cooky?"

"This book by Gypsy Rose Lee—the cover keeps coming off!"

"Just ignore him, Mr. Wells."

"This is the thing Uncle Rufe has in the city, maw. You
pound it and heat comes out."

Drawn by Louis Jamme

"Tell me, is the couch too low for you people?"

"I washed his mouth out with soap, and *then* you should
have heard what he called me."

"Wel-l-l-l, hel-lo! We were just talking about you!"

"Bad eyes."

"He hasn't made much headway since we were here last."

"Checking out, Private Quinn?"

"Mr. Hobbs, we really feel that you deserve a sack."

"We've relaxed our requirements just a bit."

"It used to scare me. Now I just think of next year's taxes and shove off."

"Stinks, doesn't it?"

"Oh, boy! Can't you just picture her in a sweater?"

"They've landed—and the situation is out of hand again!"

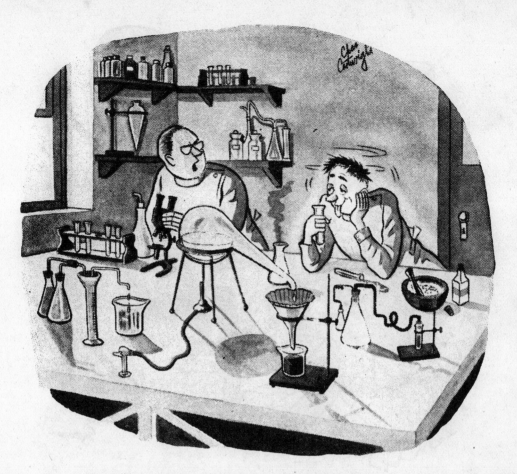

"Are you developing something to shorten the war, Henson, or just to make it seem shorter?"

Drawn by Richter

"For heaven's sake ask him to play! He's been holding that
darn thing all evening."

"Okay! it's all yours."

"He said his first word today!"

"And don't you dare repeat it!"

"Yes, sir; what can I do for you?"

"Remember how we used to talk about a girl for you and
a boy for me?"

"He explained to me that he's with Army Intelligence."

"Not lately—but I'm reading a good one, now."

"We had a whirlwind courtship—then he blew!"

LISTENING BOOTHS

LATEST SWING Records

Richter

"Nothing, thanks, we're just browsing."

ACME PRODUCTS

George Rechas

"Quick, Miss Blake, get me the file on what's-his-name, who did business with J. B. something-or-other, back in nineteen-thirty-five or thereabouts."

"Shave!"

"How soon does he start being a constant source of joy
and amusement?"

"Wait, let's watch this! It ought to be pretty good."

"There's your caddie now, and I believe he's found your ball."

"Now this part is where the fleeing fawn, wounded and beset by dangers on every side, pauses at a pool for refreshment."

"Mr. and . . . WOW!
. . . Mrs. Van Allen."

"Okay! She can't act, she can't sing, she can't dance! Now
will you shut up and let me enjoy myself?"

"He's like that from morning to night—busy, busy, busy!'

Little Lulu

Drawn by Marge

COLIN ALLEN

"What's the matter with the one you've got on? All it needs is a little water and sunshine!"

LAWRENCE LA RIAR

"And now, ladies and gentlemen, Mr. Tripowsky insists
on playing one of his own compositions!"

"Suppose we refund
your money, send you
another one, without
charge, close the store
and have the owner shot
—would that be satis-
factory?"

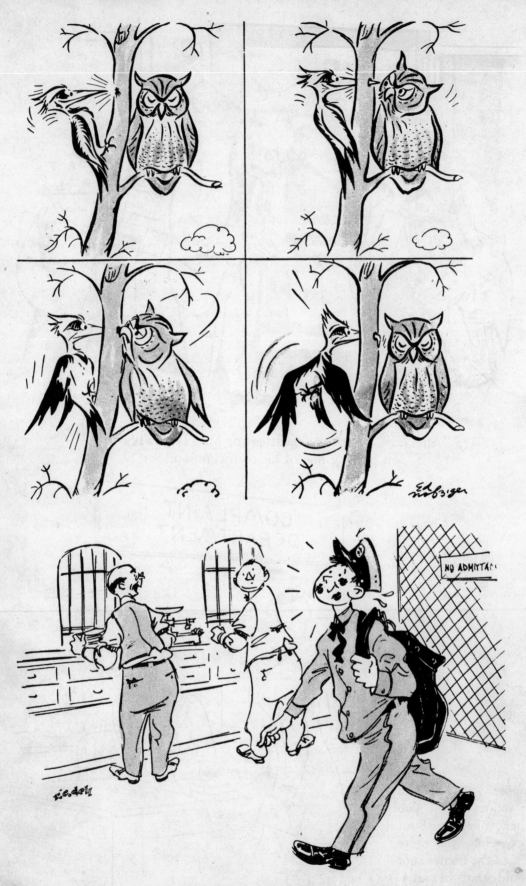

"I guess he must've delivered mostly *good* news today."

"Teach him something else. Every time you say 'Heel,' he sits and looks at me."

"Friend—ally, buddy, pal, chum, well-wisher—"

Drawn by Chas. Cartwright

"Look, dear, I only *own* a defense factory—I don't *work* in one!"

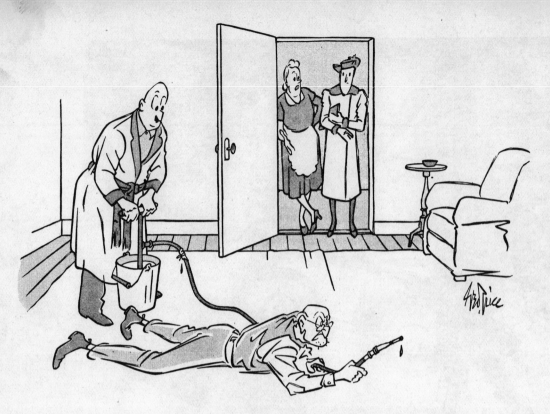

"They haven't relaxed an instant since the morning of December seventh."

"Clinton's been stationed on a mosquito boat!"

"Tell me straight, Dave—she gonna be okay?"

"Have you heard about this new cheese, containing vitamin B$_1$?"

"Taxi!"

"All clear!"

"Mamma!!!"

"This is what I get for drinking coffee for breakfast."

"Oh, that's all right—I've already been paid by her father."

"That's Professor Watkins—Current History."

Kalbach

"Hardly any of them have trouble reading *that* chart."

Scott Brown

"He was all right until he looked back, and then he fainted."

"He blames it all on my mother; my dear mother, who
has lived with us from the day we were married and who
will be only too glad to testify that in all our quarrels I
was always in the right."

"Wow!"

"What shall I do, sir? This is the first time anything like this has happened in basic training."

"He's leaving on a ten-day pass."

"Remember, *this* time they give way to *us!*"

"Slippery, isn't it?"

JOHN BAILEY

"Remember, I must have
them Saturday, sure!"

Drawn by *Ving Fuller*

"Dis is gonna be like taking candy from a baby; eh, boys?"

"How's business?"

"They walked in here cold, and asked me to explain the game to them."

"See? There it is again! I think there's someone in there!"

"Don't disarrange that desk! I know just where everything is."

"I suppose it'll be better if we take the muzzle off and let him go back to biting again!"

"Now once more and take it easy—exhale."

"Either we've been robbed or daddy is home on a surprise furlough."

"May I play through?"

"Oh! Oh! Your furnace still out of commission, Mr. Middlesworth?"

"Now don't bother me
again!"

"I couldn't put it
down. Matter of fact,
I couldn't pick it up."

Rodney deSarro

"Them's fightin' words where I come from, mister! Er
. . . how do you feel about it in your section?"

John Bailey

"Starts quick—doesn't he?"

"Come to think of it—why ain't I in the Army?"

"Something one of the candidates said, dear?"

"Major Brunstock's here with his Walkie-Talkie."

"Hired man? No, I'm a week-end guest!"

"Jabber! Jabber! Jabber!"

"Let's put it this way, Mr. Edwards: Just where did you expect to be at forty? And what's wrong with Joe's?"

"Best darned supply sergeant I ever saw."

"Junior's going to a 'Bash' with his 'Bundle-Bunny' . . .
I wonder if that's good?"

"Well, if it's dealer's choice
I say 'Old Maid'!"

"I don't like square corners,
see!"

"Good news, senator! I have a tax system figured out for next year that NOBODY will understand!"

"It's their large economomy size."

"Yes, but sardines are dead and don't mind it."

THE LITTLE SCOUTS

"I'd start right in by apologizing."

"It's all right—they're with me."

"Yes, it *is* a silly way to eat grapes."

Chon Day

W. Middlecamp

"Well, as I was saying—"

"Selective Service? Would you kindly select five or six men to come to a birthday party next Thursday?"

"I'm plodding along at a safe and sane thirty-five when
suddenly a gust of wind catches me!"

"So this is the supper I would have spoiled if I had bought
a soda at four-thirty."

"Hooray! This balances the books at the First National
Bank!"

"Wow, what a hectic day! Never again!"

"My composition is entitled 'Australia, the Land Down Under.'"

"What'll I do? They keep yelling, 'Put it on.'"

"I've heard of sailors not knowing how to *swim*, but this is too much!"

"Come on, sonny, think hard. What regiment are you from?"

"Ask me how I like them . . . go on, ask me . . . just ask me once!"

—GARRITY—

Haenigsen

"We all feel that Andrew outdid himself."

"There's a puzzling technicality here as to whether Hogan is in or out of the ring!"

'I said 'Hello.''

"She hung up on me again— but I'll get her to talk to me if it takes all night!"

"Remember the melon you sold me yesterday?"

Drawn by Barbara Shermund

"Er—isn't there some *other* way to get to the diner?"

"Is this why mother warned us against going to men's apartments?"

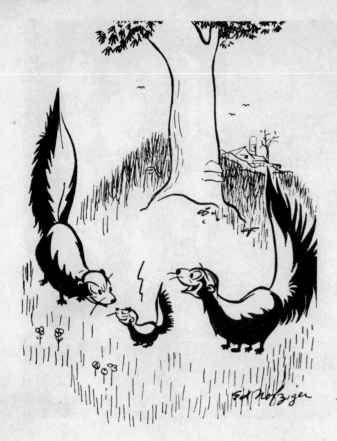

"He's beginning to smell a little already!"

"Well, before I make an appointment, I'd like to know if there's any chance of *this* doctor being called to the Army before next March."

"Why?"

"Don't worry—I'll be waiting for you."

PVT. GEO. SMITH

"Couldn't you just *put* it in?"

BILL KING

"Well, frankly, if he's in the armed forces, you don't need anything at all."

"Assuming my theory is correct, when I add the contents of this vial, the whole damn thing should blow up in my face."

"We got her from Detroit for two pitchers, a catcher and an outfielder."

"We're rather proud of it—your Aunt Lydia trompled
the grapes herself."

Little Lulu

①

②

④

③

⑤

⑥

Ted Key

"Don't care for spinach, eh?"

"Points, points, points, points!"

"Either talk louder so I can hear it all, or lower so I'll
lose interest!"

COLIN ALLEN

"I thought I'd better call you, doctor. We started playing some parlor games and—"

"Here goes the game, the ice, Mr. Johnson's disposition—
and the hike we'd planned for this afternoon!"

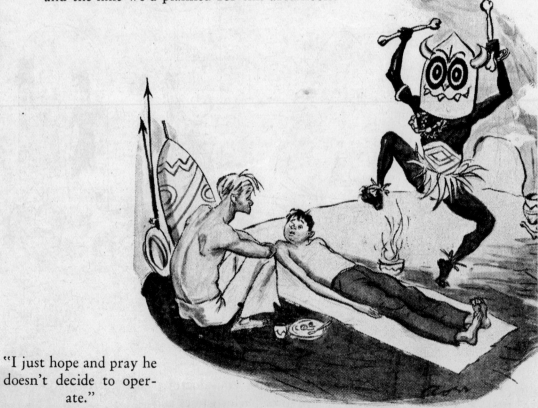

"I just hope and pray he
doesn't decide to oper-
ate."

"The nurse just stuck her head out and gave me this—the
Victory sign, I trust."

"Back home, by this time in the morning I'd have the
stove a-goin', breakfast ate, fed the chickens and pigs and
done all the milkin'."

"I understand she's his inspiration."

"This is Mr. Thompson—c'est la guerre!"

"The dean said all my troubles are caused by the pencils I use . . . too much eyebrow and not enough lead."

"Tell Mrs. Hornaday about the African customs that fascinated you."

JOHN ROSOL

GEORGE RECKAS

"Then in addition to being general manager, there will be
a few little 'extracurricular' things for you to do!"

"I guess it's just a little
too thrilling."

"Wanta see me make a guy superstitious?"

"Mark my words, Tettley—the Lone Ranger will one day involve himself inextricably, Tonto notwithstanding."

"It wouldn't surprise me if it was the very last one in the file."

"Why, Mr. Wilson, you should be under 'W.'"

"I represent the Federal Manpower Commission. How are
you fixed for help?"

"Quiet, please! I work nights!"

"Of course, nobody really wanted a dehydrated elephant, but it's nice to see what we can do."

"Mr. Foley, remember a couple of days ago when I told you the Army wanted me? Er . . . I was rejected."

"So mamma's little man practiced his lessons every day while mamma was away!"

"Oh, come now, Private Jones, at ease!"

"There must be some easier way to meet lifeguards!"

"I was out with a fellow like that once when I was sixteen."

THIS *AIN'T* THE ARMY

"*Wow!*"

"But I *am* wearing the sweater you knitted for me. I've got it on *under my shirt!*"

Richter

"Before we begin, I suppose I ought to explain a few special rules."

Rodney deSARRO

"He said his first sentence just now—'E pluribus unum'!"

"Don't miss this—that drawer sticks a little, then *whooshes* out."

"I bet you think I'm just an old stick-in-the-mud!"

"Yoo-hoo! Mr. and Mrs. Smith! Your bell must be out of order! We've been ringing it for the longest time, and you haven't answered!"

"Yes?"

"All this, so that some jerk can decorate his waffles."

DRAFT BOARD NO. 38

DRAFT BOARD

BILL RUBLE

"Before I let you in, dear, do you promise to go on loving
me no matter what?"

"Me?"

"I know you're glad to get mail from home, Harkins, but honestly, I had nothing whatever to do with it!"

"Are you hurt?"

"It's my girl—I guess she misses me."

"Why, *no*, we haven't seen your husband, dear."

"Never mind the boring platitudes, bud—what's the rap?"

"For some reason, your father seems to dislike me."

"Sometimes a voice within me cries, 'Oh, the futility of it all.'"

MARRIAGE LICENSES

Drawn by Colin Allen

"I'm afraid you misunderstood. I'm NOT looking for a job as hired man; I'm making a help survey for the Government."

"In case you get bored later in the evening, *and you will,* I'll be down at the pool hall."

"Now, now, dear—in just a few minutes we'll see daddy."

"I didn't mind the black eyes . . . It was the 'one for good measure' I objected to."

"Of course, to follow my plan completely they'd have to bring everybody back to the United States and start all over."

"Look, girls, I sure hate to leave you, but that bugler's
going to wake me up any second now."

"Mamma wants you to stop saying, 'What died? What
died?'"

"I'm on stilts."

BILL KING

"When Bob Hope did this
it was a scream."

"Certainly killed the afternoon, didn't it?"

"Relax—I'm going to bed as soon as I've finished this row."

"I warned you to leave my wife out of this."

"My husband—when he was a baby, of course."

"HALF-HITCH"

BILL RUBLE

"Care for a few hands of two-handed rummy?"

Lariar

"Do you suppose my working on an assembly line had anything to do with it?"

"They're the living-room curtains, John. What did you
think they were?"

"Of course I know you're right, dear—I just want to see
if our dictionary is."

"I want it for a gift."

"That will be all, Mrs. Beal. Thank you *so* much."

"I'm a pushover for beautiful girls with brains and money."

"My problem's simple. Have you got a couple bucks that ain't workin'?"

"Call this typing? You're fired! Well—not exactly fired, but after this be a bit more careful."

"Anybody feel like
shuffleboard?"

"You watch where he buries it while I go put some water
on to boil."

"Nice stop, Albert!"

"Now let's see your pass—this time without the gestures."

"Mating season—and me with laryngitis!"

"What a day! I lost my job. I lost my billfold. My wife left me. And the Dodgers lost to the Phillies. It's unbelievable—leading by three in the eighth, and they lost to the Phillies!"

"I was chilly!"

"Take the bus home, dear?"

"Just state that the lady in question is beautiful. Never mind the gestures!"

"This is nothing—you should see Times Square on New Year's Eve!"

"Isn't she feeling well, or is that Frank Sinatra?"

"I'm not mentioning any names, but I'll bet North catches it from South for paying so much attention to West!"

"I'm sorry that I wasn't able to accept your invitations during the previous years—but, Ferbus, how would you like to invite me to your house for dinner tonight?"

DRAWN BY COLIN ALLEN

"—So then the little boy's mother said, 'No! You can't have any candy!' And then the little boy's father said, 'No! You can't have any candy!' And then the little boy went to his grandma and she said, 'You can have all the candy you want—and ice cream and cookies and toys too!' So—"

"The committee from Washington to see you, sir."

"Seems a shame to waste any of it!"

"Since I got here the only person I've seen from home that
I knew was Roosevelt!"

"I picked up people's Exhibit A and said to the deceased, 'Don't come near!' However, brandishing defendant's Exhibit 3, he slowly advanced, whereupon the incident referred to in the indictment occurred."

"We're one big happy family again, mother, now that their husbands are drafted."

"I wouldn't overdo it—just
act cheerful!"

"I think it was wonderful of
you to try and explain it to
me."

DAVE GERARD

"Let's see now, Helda—Mr. Cramer will be eating dinner, Eloise is going on night shift so she'll want breakfast, and you and I will be having lunch."

"Yeah? Come on down to the rumpus room and say that!"

"Turn your radio down, you big ape, my wife says."

"I'm not buying anything! I just don't wanna miss it when she gets fed up!"

"It isn't so much ice cream I dream about—it's more of a
frozen custard."

". . . Over boy, roll over, roll over boy, he'll do it in a minute, over boy, roll over, over boy, roll over, roll over boy, over, show 'em how you roll over boy, over boy, he'll do it in a minute, over boy . . ."

"I must tell you, we'll soon be hearing the patter of little feet!"

"It's just a passing thought, but do you think we could consult Mr. Anthony?"

"I wish to give myself up."

"With us, ma'am, shoes are more than something to cram feet into!"

"It's the man from upstairs again."

"Boy, what a year that was!"

"Maybe we're wasting our time—how do we know it's a
dame?"

"Maybe I put too much color in that bird and bee business!"

"I want to buy a dress for my wife."

"It's so embarrassing—when we drive into town people
yell 'Get a horse!' "

"John hasn't been buying any new clothes since he's been expecting to be drafted."

"Naw, this is 2B! You got the wrong threshold!"

"Daddy's got a steak! Daddy's got a steak!"

"Of course, what I really came in for was a set of tiddly-winks."

"There's a well-turned
ankle."

"Shoot the works!"

"See, I told you we didn't rehearse enough."

"Oh, come now, Judson!"

FRANK BEAVEN

"SILENCE! H. V. Kaltenborn!"

"Nope! What's even harder to get than a maid?"

CHARLES PLATT

"Needless to say, you're the
first woman I've seen in six
months."

"Why, of course I love you
. . . er . . . ah . . . er . . .
ah . . . Geraldine!"